SPOT THE DIFFERENCE

PaRragon

Bath · New York · Singapore · Hong Kong · Cologne · Delhi · Melbourne

First published by Parragon in 2009

Parragon
Queen Street House
4 Queen Street
Bath
BA1 1HE, UK

Design, layout and photo manipulation by

quadrum▪

All images © iStock

ISBN: 978-1-4075-8121-7

Printed in Malaysia

Contents

SOLVING THE PUZZLES

1. Give yourself a minute to carefully scrutinise each of the pictures.
2. Then, start comparing them with each other.
3. Every time you spot a difference in a picture, make sure to mark it out.
4. Once you think you are done, cross check your findings with the answers provided at the back of the book.

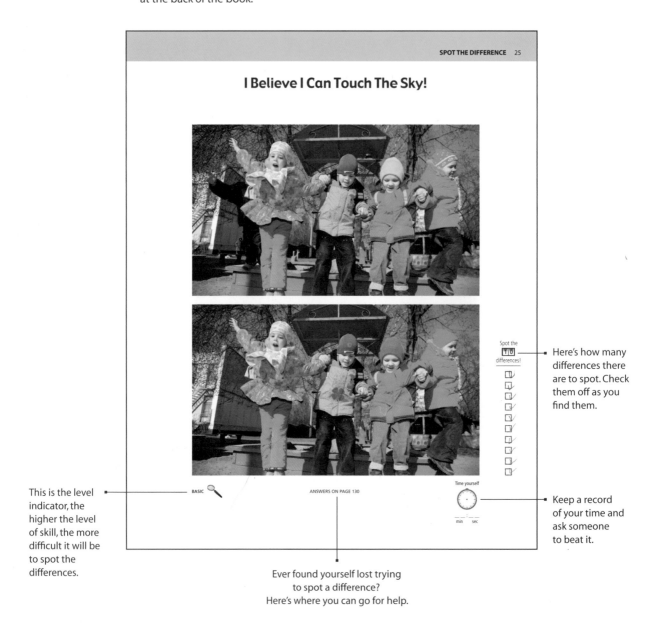

This is the level indicator, the higher the level of skill, the more difficult it will be to spot the differences.

Here's how many differences there are to spot. Check them off as you find them.

Keep a record of your time and ask someone to beat it.

Ever found yourself lost trying to spot a difference? Here's where you can go for help.

1. Take a minute to carefully scrutinise all six images.
2. Five of these pictures are exactly the same. One is just a little different. Can you find the odd one?
3. Don't forget to time yourself!

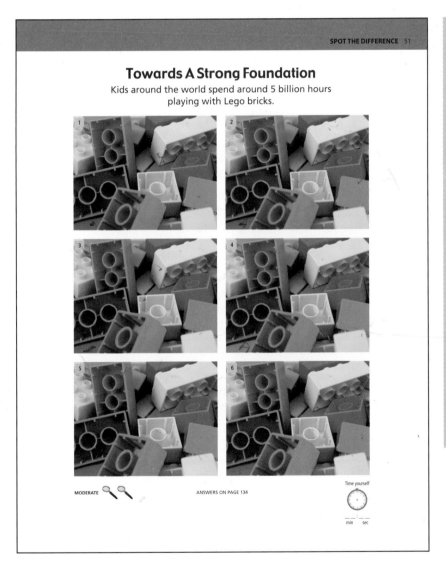

Towards A Strong Foundation
Kids around the world spend around 5 billion hours playing with Lego bricks.

MODERATE   ANSWERS ON PAGE 134   Time yourself

5	EXTREME
4	ADVANCED
3	CHALLENGING
2	MODERATE
1	BASIC

COLOR CODED SECTIONS

These color coded sections will help you identify the level of difficulty. So keep going up the elevator by challenging yourself to master these five levels.

Happy Spotting...

BASIC

Calling all
you rookies
and veterans,
young and
old: Try these
puzzles and see
how good you
actually are.

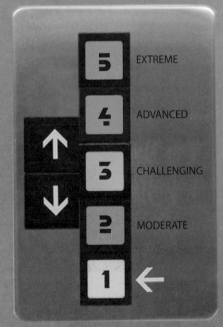

5 EXTREME

4 ADVANCED

3 CHALLENGING

2 MODERATE

1

Family Ties

The construction of the Sagrada Familia began in 1882 and is expected to be completed in 2026!

BASIC

Spot the
08
differences!

BASIC

ANSWERS ON PAGE 128

Time yourself

__ __ : __ __
min   sec

Summer Fun!

Did you know that fighting cocks were given a mixture of spirits by their trainers before a fight? This mixture was known as "cocks-ale."

Spot the

differences!

Time yourself

___ : ___
min   sec

Rock On!

See if you can spot all the changes to this picture of the ancient burial ground.

Spot the

0 7

differences!

☐
☐
☐
☐
☐
☐
☐

Time yourself

__ __ : __ __
min   sec

A Rolling Stone Gathers No Moss

There's no rolling stone in this image, but there are differences—see if you can find them all.

Spot the
1 2
differences!

☐
☐
☐
☐
☐
☐
☐
☐
☐
☐
☐
☐

BASIC

ANSWERS ON PAGE 128

Time yourself

_ _ : _ _
min   sec

Learning Can Be Fun!

"A single conversation with a wise man is better than ten years of study." – Chinese Proverb

Spot the
08
differences!

ANSWERS ON PAGE 128

Time yourself

__ __ : __ __
min   sec

Metamorphosis

The life span of a butterfly is anywhere from a week to nearly a year depending on the species. Try and spot which image is the odd one.

BASIC

ANSWERS ON PAGE 128

Time yourself

__ : __
min   sec

Wanna Play Ball?

One of these images is different. Can you tell which one?

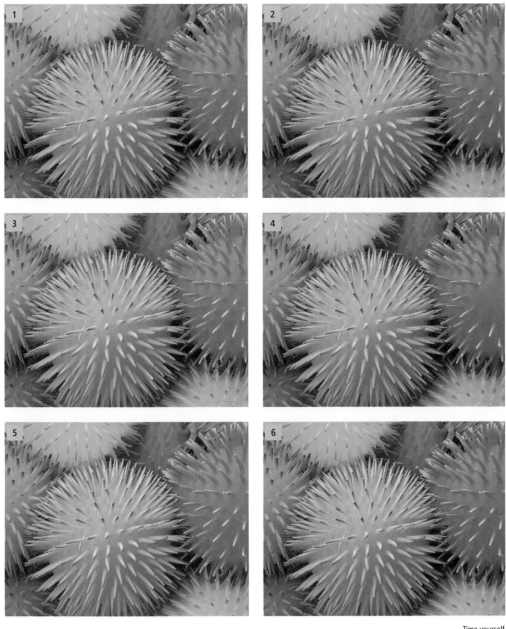

If They Fit, Buy 'Em In Every Color!

Spot the
0 7
differences!

☐
☐
☐
☐
☐
☐
☐

BASIC

ANSWERS ON PAGE 129

Time yourself

__ __ : __ __
min   sec

That's A Capitol Suggestion!

Spot the
0 7
differences!

☐
☐
☐
☐
☐
☐
☐

Time yourself

__ __ : __ __
min   sec

BASIC

ANSWERS ON PAGE 129

Home Sweet Home

The oldest house in the world is approximately from 10,000 BC and was made of mammoth bones, found at Mezhirich in Ukraine.

Spot the

differences!

BASIC

ANSWERS ON PAGE 129

Time yourself

__ __ : __ __
min   sec

Three's Company

Try and find all differences in these two images.

Spot the

0 6

differences!

Time yourself

__ __ : __ __
min   sec

Row, Row, Row Your Boat

Kayaks had been discovered by Europeans as late as the early 20th century. Find all the changes to the Kayaks images.

BASIC

Spot the

differences!

☐
☐
☐
☐
☐
☐
☐
☐

BASIC

ANSWERS ON PAGE 129

Time yourself

__ __ : __ __
min   sec

United Colors Of The World!

"A friend is one of the nicest things you can have, and one of the best things you can be."   – Douglas Pagels

Spot the

differences!

☐
☐
☐
☐
☐
☐
☐
☐
☐

Time yourself

__ __ : __ __
min   sec

Happy Feet

The smallest penguin species is the Little Blue Penguin which stands around 16 inches tall and weighs 2¼ lbs.

Spot the

0 7

differences!

☐
☐
☐
☐
☐
☐
☐

Time yourself

__ __ : __ __
min   sec

This Ain't No London Bridge!

Spot the

differences!

BASIC

ANSWERS ON PAGE 130

Time yourself

__ __ : __ __
min   sec

I Believe I Can Touch The Sky!

Spot the
10
differences!

BASIC

ANSWERS ON PAGE 130

Time yourself

___ __ : __ ___
min   sec

Make A Wish

Try and find the odd man out from the six cake images.

BASIC

ANSWERS ON PAGE 130

Time yourself

__ __ : __ __
min   sec

How's This For A Fashion Statement?

All the umbrellas are not the same. Look carefully to find the odd one out.

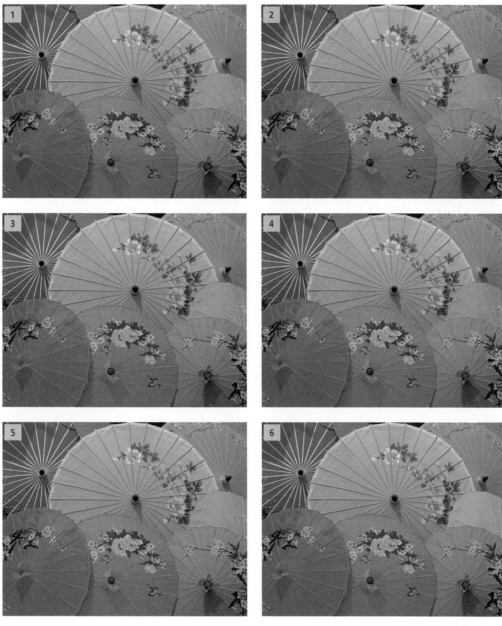

BASIC   ANSWERS ON PAGE 130

Time yourself

__ __ : __ __
min   sec

MODERATE

Now that you have figured out what to do, try your hand at these slightly tougher puzzles.

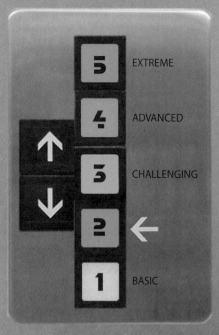

5 EXTREME

4 ADVANCED

3 CHALLENGING

2 ←

1 BASIC

In God We Trust

The Vasily Blazhenny Church was built by an Italian architect who was blinded so he could never create anything equal to it.

MODERATE

Spot the
0 9
differences!

☐
☐
☐
☐
☐
☐
☐
☐
☐

MODERATE

ANSWERS ON PAGE 131

Time yourself

__ __ : __ __
min   sec

Quiet Reflections

More than 1,000 species of animals live in ponds—although you won't find them all here! Try and see if you can spot the differences.

Spot the
0 7
differences!

☐
☐
☐
☐
☐
☐
☐

MODERATE

ANSWERS ON PAGE 131

Time yourself

__ __ : __ __
min   sec

Picture Perfect!

Just the setting for that special quiet time you need.

Spot the
0 9
differences!

MODERATE

ANSWERS ON PAGE 131

Time yourself

__ __ : __ __
min   sec

Fit For A King

The Grand Palace is not actually a palace but a complex
of royal buildings.

Spot the

differences!

 MODERATE

ANSWERS ON PAGE 131

Time yourself

_ _ : _ _
min   sec

Loud Enough To Scare The Loch Ness Monster!

Bagpipes were once used by the Scots to frighten away their enemies on the battlefield.

Spot the
0 8
differences!

Time yourself

__ __ : __ __
min   sec

Zen'd Out!

All the trays are not alike. Try and see if you can spot the odd one out.

MODERATE

ANSWERS ON PAGE 131

Time yourself

__ __ : __ __
min sec

Sweets For My Sweet!

These candy images look yummy, yet they are all not the same. See if you can spot the odd one out.

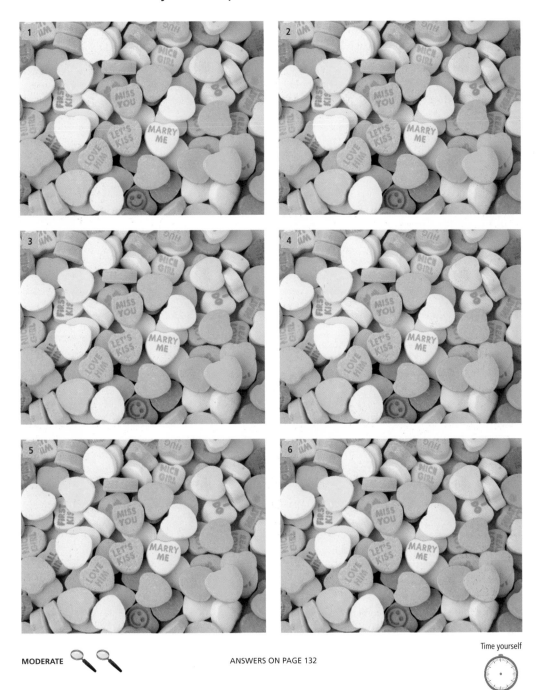

MODERATE

ANSWERS ON PAGE 132

Time yourself

__ : __
min   sec

Perfect Patio!

Here's the perfect back yard for you...however, there is something amiss. Try and see if you can spot the differences.

Spot the
1 0
differences!

☐
☐
☐
☐
☐
☐
☐
☐
☐
☐

MODERATE

ANSWERS ON PAGE 132

Time yourself

__ __ : __ __
min   sec

Playing To Win

The word "checkmate" comes from the Persian phrase "shah mat," which means "the king is defeated".

Spot the
0 7
differences!

 MODERATE

ANSWERS ON PAGE 132

Time yourself

__ __ : __ __
min   sec

Hope You Have A Huge Credit Limit!

Rodeo Drive is a three-block long stretch of boutiques in Beverly Hills that house the world's most exclusive and well-known designers.

Spot the

differences!

☐
☐
☐
☐
☐
☐
☐

 MODERATE

ANSWERS ON PAGE 132

Time yourself

__ : __ __
min   sec

Hey...Look What I Made Today!

"Life is a succession of lessons, which must be lived to be understood." – Ralph Waldo Emerson

Spot the
1 0
differences!

MODERATE

ANSWERS ON PAGE 132

Time yourself

___ : ___
min   sec

Lean On Me!

Did you know that after restoration work between 1990 and 2001, the Leaning Tower of Pisa leans at an angle of 3.99 degrees?

MODERATE

Spot the
0 8
differences!

MODERATE

ANSWERS ON PAGE 132

Time yourself

___ ___ : ___ ___
min   sec

Trick Or Treat?

Did you know that on Halloween, Irish peasants used to beg
the rich for food?

Spot the
07
differences!

☐
☐
☐
☐
☐
☐
☐

MODERATE

ANSWERS ON PAGE 133

Time yourself

__ __ : __ __
min   sec

Love Can Work Wonders

Emperor Shah Jahan built this white marble wonder in memory of his beloved wife Mumtaz Mahal.

Spot the
0 9
differences!

MODERATE

ANSWERS ON PAGE 133

Time yourself

__ __ : __ __
min   sec

In Holy Company

The interior of the Sultan Ahmed Mosque in Istanbul is lined with more than 20,000 handmade ceramic tiles.

Spot the

differences!

MODERATE

ANSWERS ON PAGE 133

Time yourself

__ __ : __ __
min   sec

Eat Your Veggies!

See if you can see your favorite vegetable when you're looking for the changes in the two images.

Spot the
0 7
differences!

MODERATE

ANSWERS ON PAGE 133

Time yourself

_ _ : _ _
min   sec

Down Rodeo Drive

Welcome to the epicenter of luxury fashion!

Spot the

differences!

The Slower, The Better

Spot the
 0 7
differences!

MODERATE

ANSWERS ON PAGE 133

Time yourself

__ __ : __ __
min   sec

That's Hot!

There are probably 400 different chillies grown and are one of the most widely cultivated crops from the Far East to India to Mexico.

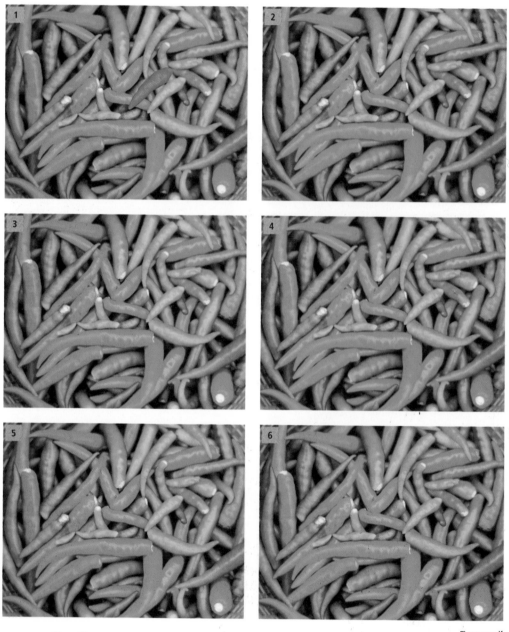

MODERATE

ANSWERS ON PAGE 134

Time yourself

__ __ : __ __
min   sec

Toward A Strong Foundation

Kids all over the world spend around 5 billion hours
playing with Lego blocks.

MODERATE

ANSWERS ON PAGE 134

Time yourself

__ __ : __ __
min   sec

CHALLENGING

Now the going gets tough! Time to pit your brains against our latest challenges.

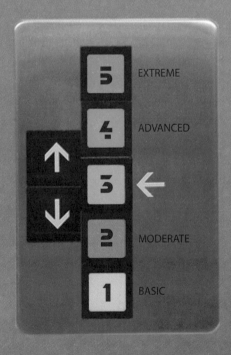

5 — EXTREME

4 — ADVANCED

3 ←

2 — MODERATE

1 — BASIC

Eat Healthy, Think Healthy

Work up an appetite looking for all the changes in this delicious image.

CHALLENGING

Spot the
0 7
differences!

☐
☐
☐
☐
☐
☐
☐

CHALLENGING

ANSWERS ON PAGE 134

Time yourself

__ __ : __ __
min   sec

Back To Square One

St. Peter's Square has a combination of both Egyptian and Italian architecture.

Spot the

differences!

ANSWERS ON PAGE 134

CHALLENGING

Time yourself

__ __ : __ __
min   sec

Flower Power!

These flowers are pretty but not all the same. See if you can find the changes.

Spot the

08

differences!

CHALLENGING

ANSWERS ON PAGE 134

Time yourself

__ __ : __ __
min   sec

Try Getting Out Of This One!

The Bugatti Type 41 Royale is the world's most expensive car and is valued at $10 million.

Spot the
0 8
differences!

☐
☐
☐
☐
☐
☐
☐
☐

CHALLENGING

ANSWERS ON PAGE 134

Time yourself

__ __ : __ __
min   sec

Santa Claus Is Coming To Town

In Sweden, children leave brownies and not milk and cookies out for Santa Claus on Christmas Eve.

Spot the

differences!

CHALLENGING

ANSWERS ON PAGE 135

Time yourself

___ : ___
min   sec

A Jackpot Win!

Augustus Caesar conducted the first known public lottery for a community cause, raising funds for repair work in the city of Rome.

CHALLENGING

ANSWERS ON PAGE 135

Time yourself

__ __ : __ __
min   sec

My Hairstyle Is Definitely Better!

See if you can spot the unique one out.

CHALLENGING

ANSWERS ON PAGE 135

Time yourself

__ __ : __ __
min   sec

May The Best Team Win

"The true object of all human life is play. Earth is a task garden; heaven is a playground." – G.K. Chesterton

Spot the

differences!

CHALLENGING

ANSWERS ON PAGE 135

Time yourself

__ __ : __ __
min   sec

God's Own Country

Did you know that the Vatican City is the smallest country in the world in terms of area and population?

Spot the
0 8
differences!

CHALLENGING

ANSWERS ON PAGE 135

Time yourself

__ : __
min   sec

To Bee Or Not To Bee!

The honeybee's wings stroke 11,400 times per minute, thus making their distinctive buzz.

Spot the
0 8
differences!

☐
☐
☐
☐
☐
☐
☐
☐

CHALLENGING    ANSWERS ON PAGE 135

Time yourself

__ __ : __ __
min   sec

Stop – Men At Work!

"One generation plants the trees, and another gets the shade."
– Anonymous

Spot the
0 8
differences!

☐
☐
☐
☐
☐
☐
☐
☐

CHALLENGING

ANSWERS ON PAGE 136

Time yourself

_ _ : _ _
min   sec

Pump Up The Jam!

Look for all the changes on these wheels of steel.

CHALLENGING

Spot the
0 8
differences!

CHALLENGING

ANSWERS ON PAGE 136

Time yourself

__ __ : __ __
min   sec

Ride 'Em Cowboy!

The word "cowboy" is taken from the Spanish "vaquero" meaning an individual who managed cattle while on horseback. Yee ha!

Spot the

differences!

CHALLENGING

ANSWERS ON PAGE 136

Time yourself

__ __ : __ __
min   sec

A Pitch Off The Old Block!

Most global NGOs maintain an emergency stockpile of tents strategically placed all over the world to service their requirements.

Spot the

0 9

differences!

Time yourself

__ __ : __ __
min   sec

Nature's Wonderful Bounty

Here's plenty to choose from...just make sure that what you pick are in both the images.

Spot the

differences!

CHALLENGING

ANSWERS ON PAGE 136

Time yourself

___ : ___
min   sec

City Heights!

"Houses mean a creation, something new, a shelter freed from the idea of a cave." – Stephen Gardiner

Spot the
0 9
differences!

CHALLENGING

ANSWERS ON PAGE 136

Time yourself

__ __ : __ __
min   sec

Hats Off!

Did you know that in the Philippines, the use of rice paddies can be traced to prehistoric times?

Spot the
0 6
differences!

☐
☐
☐
☐
☐
☐

CHALLENGING

ANSWERS ON PAGE 137

Time yourself

___ : ___
min   sec

Mall Rat!

"Whoever said money can't buy happiness simply didn't know where to go shopping." – Bo Derek

Spot the
0 7
differences!

☐
☐
☐
☐
☐
☐
☐

Time yourself

__ __ : __ __
min   sec

Water Babies!

Did you know that divers in the 1300s made goggles
from polished, clear tortoise shell?

CHALLENGING

ANSWERS ON PAGE 137

Time yourself

__ __ : __ __
min   sec

Canned It

The first tin cans were so thick they had to be hammered open.

ANSWERS ON PAGE 137

CHALLENGING

Time yourself

__ __ : __ __
min   sec

ADVANCED

Kudos on
cracking the
earlier puzzles.
Now is your
chance to raise
the bar further.

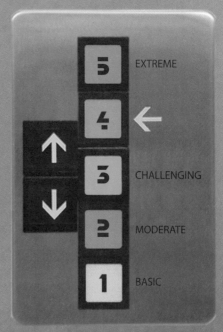

5 — EXTREME

4 ←

3 — CHALLENGING

2 — MODERATE

1 — BASIC

It's A Bargain!

Popular belief is that the name "flea market" was coined as both the buyers and sellers might have been as active as fleas.

ADVANCED

Spot the
0 7
differences!

☐
☐
☐
☐
☐
☐
☐

ADVANCED

ANSWERS ON PAGE 137

Time yourself

__ __ : __ __
min   sec

Counting Colors Of The Rainbow...

Did you know that life in the seas began 3.1 billion to 3.4 billion years ago?

Spot the

differences!

ADVANCED

ANSWERS ON PAGE137

Time yourself

__ __ : __ __
min   sec

Unlimited Learning!

"The aim of education is the knowledge not of fact, but of values."
– Dean William R. Inge

Spot the

differences!

ADVANCED

ANSWERS ON PAGE 138

Time yourself

__ __ : __ __
min   sec

How Annoying!

See if you can find all the differences among this bothered bunch.

Spot the
10
differences!

ADVANCED

ANSWERS ON PAGE138

Time yourself

___ : ___
min   sec

Adrenaline Junkies

Spot the
0 7
differences!

ADVANCED

ANSWERS ON PAGE 138

Time yourself

__ __ : __ __
min   sec

For Queen And Country

The Abbey was first founded in 616 on the present site based on a "tradition" that a fisherman saw a vision of Saint Peter near the site.

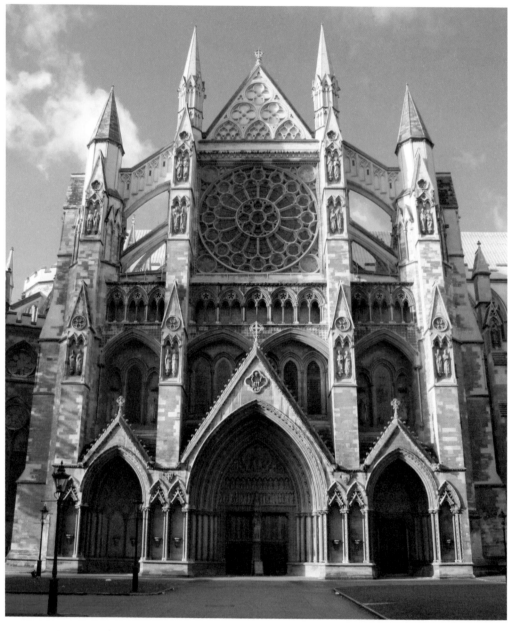

ADVANCED

Spot the

0 6

differences!

Time yourself

__ __ : __ __
min   sec

ADVANCED   ANSWERS ON PAGE 138

Off And Running!

"There is no secret so close as that between a rider and his horse."
– R.S. Surtees

Spot the
0|7
differences!

☐
☐
☐
☐
☐
☐
☐

ADVANCED 🔍🔍🔍🔍   ANSWERS ON PAGE 138

Time yourself

_ _ : _ _
min   sec

A Matter Of Taste

The grape is one of the oldest fruits to be cultivated, going back as far as biblical times.

Spot the

differences!

ADVANCED

ANSWERS ON PAGE 138

Time yourself

___ : ___
min   sec

God Save The Queen

Windsor Castle is the largest inhabited castle in the world.

Spot the
10
differences!

ADVANCED

ANSWERS ON PAGE 139

Time yourself

__ : __
min   sec

Say Cheese!

"We learn by teaching."   – James Howell

Spot the
 0 7
differences!

ADVANCED    ANSWERS ON PAGE 139

Time yourself

__ __ : __ __
min   sec

Forward March!

Did you know that the U.S.A has produced a stamp made out of plastic?

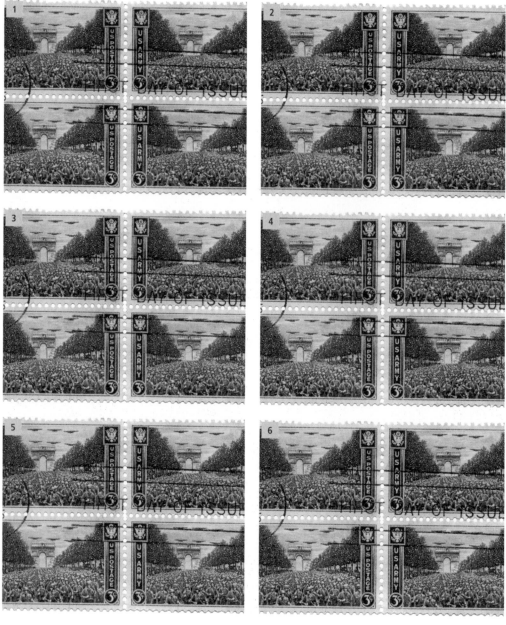

Gimme Back What's Mine!

Even though all the dogs vary greatly in appearance, they are identical in anatomy.

ADVANCED

ANSWERS ON PAGE139

Time yourself

_ _ : _ _
min   sec

Classroom Portrait

"Learning is a treasure that will follow its owner everywhere."
– Anonymous

ADVANCED

Spot the
0 9
differences!

☐
☐
☐
☐
☐
☐
☐
☐
☐

ADVANCED

ANSWERS ON PAGE139

Time yourself

___ ___ : ___ ___
min   sec

Which Color Do You Want To Choose?

Did you know that Newton identified light as the source of all color sensation?

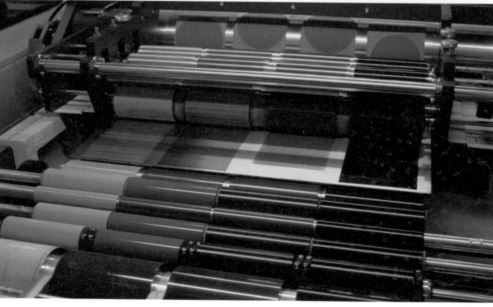

Spot the
0 8
differences!

☐
☐
☐
☐
☐
☐
☐
☐

ADVANCED

ANSWERS ON PAGE 139

Time yourself

__ __ : __ __
min   sec

Up, Up And Away!

"Friendship isn't a big thing—it's a million little things."
– Anonymous

Spot the
0 8
differences!

☐
☐
☐
☐
☐
☐
☐
☐

ADVANCED

ANSWERS ON PAGE 140

Time yourself

__ __ : __ __
min   sec

If One Can, Toucan!

Toucans sleep in holes that are in trees. If they don't fit, they turn themselves into a feathery ball to make their body smaller.

Spot the differences!

ADVANCED

ANSWERS ON PAGE 140

Time yourself

__ : __
min   sec

Saying It With Flowers

Although tulips are associated with Holland, both the flower and its name actually originated in the Persian empire.

Spot the
08
differences!

ADVANCED

ANSWERS ON PAGE 140

Time yourself

___:___
min   sec

Talk About Misplaced Patriotism!

The word "flag" is derived from the old Saxon word "fflaken" which means to fly or to float in the air.

Spot the differences!

ADVANCED    ANSWERS ON PAGE 140

Time yourself

__ __ : __ __
min   sec

Table For One?

Did you know that another name for tabletop arrangements is "Tablescapes"?

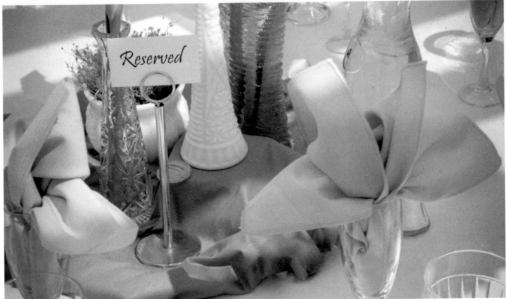

Spot the

08

differences!

☐
☐
☐
☐
☐
☐
☐
☐

ADVANCED

ANSWERS ON PAGE140

Time yourself

__ __ : __ __
min   sec

Message In A Bottle

Though all the bottles look alike, there is an odd image out there.
See if you can find it.

ADVANCED

ANSWERS ON PAGE 140

Time yourself

__ __ : __ __
min   sec

Masquerade Party!

Did you know that the Venice Carnival is the most internationally known festival celebrated in Italy, as well as one of the oldest?

ADVANCED    ANSWERS ON PAGE 141

Time yourself

__ __ : __ __
min   sec

Hurray, you're almost a grand master...if you crack a few more, you're the best!

5 ←
4 ADVANCED
3 CHALLENGING
2 MODERATE
1 BASIC

Are You On The Right Track?

It was the humble compass that brought about accurate sea travel in Europe.

EXTREME

Spot the
0 7
differences!

EXTREME

ANSWERS ON PAGE 141

Time yourself

__ : __
min   sec

A Walk In The Crowd

Find all the changes and you'll be head and shoulders above the rest.

Spot the
09
differences!

☐
☐
☐
☐
☐
☐
☐
☐
☐

EXTREME

ANSWERS ON PAGE 141

Time yourself

__ __ : __ __
min   sec

Shop Till You Drop!

Harrods occupies a 4.5-acre site and is over one million square feet.

Spot the

1 0

differences!

☐
☐
☐
☐
☐
☐
☐
☐
☐
☐

EXTREME

ANSWERS ON PAGE 141

Time yourself

__ __ : __ __
min   sec

Chasing The Bulls And Bears

All the numbers may look alike but there are changes in both the images. Look carefully and see if you can spot all the differences.

Spot the
0 7
differences!

☐
☐
☐
☐
☐
☐
☐

EXTREME

ANSWERS ON PAGE 141

Time yourself

__ __ : __ __
min   sec

London Calling!

Despite the Gherkin Skyscraper's overall curved glass shape, there is only one piece of curved glass on the building; right on top.

Spot the
0 9
differences!

EXTREME    ANSWERS ON PAGE 141

Time yourself

__ __ : __ __
min   sec

That's What I Call Being Book Smart

Between 1986 and 1996, Brazilian author Jose Carlos Ryoki de Alpoim Inoue had a massive 1,058 novels published.

EXTREME

Spot the
0 7
differences!

☐
☐
☐
☐
☐
☐
☐

EXTREME    ANSWERS ON PAGE 142

Time yourself

__ __ : __ __
min   sec

Casino Royale

The term "Casino" originally meant a small villa or pavilion built for pleasure, usually in the grounds of a larger Italian villa or palazzo.

Spot the

differences!

EXTREME    ANSWERS ON PAGE 142

Time yourself

__ __ : __ __
min   sec

Swimming With The Fish

Did you know that there are approximately 27,000 known species of fish, making them the most diverse group of vertebrates?

Spot the

differences!

EXTREME    ANSWERS ON PAGE 142

Time yourself

__ __ : __ __
min   sec

Power Dressing

Did you know that ties have been one of the most popular gifts for dads in the nearly 100 years that Father's Day has been celebrated?

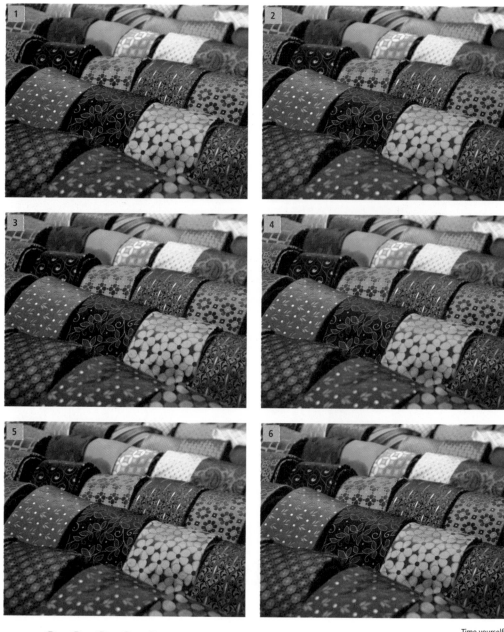

EXTREME

ANSWERS ON PAGE 142

Time yourself

__ __ : __ __
min   sec

Plenty To Choose From

Did you know that corn is an ingredient in more than 3,000 grocery products?

EXTREME

ANSWERS ON PAGE 142

Time yourself

_ _ : _ _
min   sec

Think You Can Beat This?

America's families spend more than 19 cents out of every dollar earned on transportation, an expense second only to housing.

Spot the
0 9
differences!

☐
☐
☐
☐
☐
☐
☐
☐
☐

EXTREME

ANSWERS ON PAGE 142

Time yourself

__ __ : __ __
min   sec

Aaatchoolip!

Try to stop sneezing long enough to find all the differences!

Spot the
0 8
differences!

EXTREME ANSWERS ON PAGE 143

Time yourself

__ __ : __ __
min   sec

Bottoms Up!

Take a few minutes to find all the changes and then celebrate with a glass of bubbly!

EXTREME

Spot the
0 9
differences!

☐
☐
☐
☐
☐
☐
☐
☐
☐

EXTREME

ANSWERS ON PAGE 143

Time yourself

__ __ : __ __
min   sec

Pick One, Any One

Did you know that flags are used until they are worn out and then they are destroyed, preferably by burning?

Spot the

differences!

EXTREME    ANSWERS ON PAGE 143

Time yourself

__ __ : __ __
min   sec

e = mc²

When Einstein was five years old and ill in bed, his father showed him a compass, which is said to have sparked his interest in science.

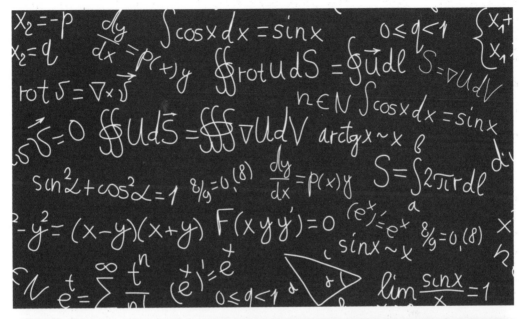

Spot the

11

differences!

☐
☐
☐
☐
☐
☐
☐
☐
☐

Time yourself

__ : __

min   sec

Acoustically Sound!

Opera started in Italy at the end of the 16th century (with Jacopo Peri's lost Dafne, produced in Florence around 1597).

Spot the
08
differences!

EXTREME

ANSWERS ON PAGE 143

Time yourself

__ __ : __ __
min   sec

Coffee Anyone?

Did you know that the use of coffee as a beverage is about
700 years old?

Spot the
1 0
differences!

EXTREME   ANSWERS ON PAGE 143

Time yourself

__ __ : __ __
min   sec

You May Now Kiss The Bride

In ancient Greece and Rome, the wedding bouquet was not made up of flowers but a pungent mix of garlic and herbs or grains.

Spot the differences!

☐
☐
☐
☐
☐
☐
☐
☐
☐
☐

EXTREME    ANSWERS ON PAGE 144

Time yourself

__ __ : __ __
min   sec

Read The Writing On The Wall!

Graffiti has existed since ancient times, with examples going all the way back to ancient Greece and the Roman Empire.

Spot the
0 8
differences!

EXTREME ANSWERS ON PAGE 144

Time yourself

__ : __
min   sec

They Come In Different Sizes!

The earliest known clear glass is a vase found in Assyria, dating from around 800 BC, which is now in the British Museum in London.

EXTREME

ANSWERS ON PAGE 144

Time yourself

__ : __
min   sec

Fire And Ice

Given as a gift, rubies are a symbol of devotion, integrity, and success.

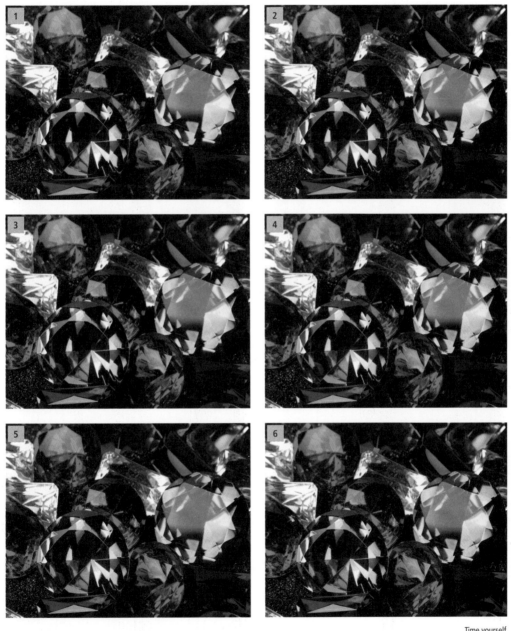

EXTREME    ANSWERS ON PAGE 144

Time yourself

__ __ : __ __
min   sec

Page 09:

Page 10:

Page 11:

Page 12:

Page 13:

Page 14:

Page 15:

Page 16:

Page 17:

Page 18:

Page 19:

Page 21:

Page 22:

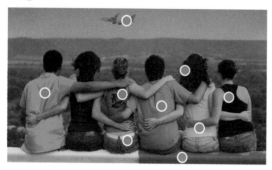

Page 23:

Page 24:

Page 25:

Page 26:

Page 27:

Page 31:

Page 32:

Page 33:

Page 34:

Page 35:

Page 36:

Page 37:

Page 38:

Page 39:

Page 40:

Page 41:

Page 43:

Page 44:

Page 45:

Page 46:

Page 47:

Page 48:

Page 49:

Page 50:

Page 51:

Page 55:

Page 56:

Page 57:

Page 58:

Page 59:

Page 60:

Page 61:

Page 62:

Page 63:

Page 64:

Page 65:

Page 67:

Page 68:

Page 69:

Page 70:

Page 71:

Page 72:

Page 73:

Page 74:

Page 75:

Page 79:

Page 80:

Page 81:

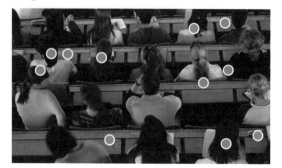

Page 82:

Page 83:

Page 85:

Page 86:

Page 87:

Page 88:

Page 89:

Page 90:

Page 91:

Page 93:

Page 94:

Page 95:

Page 96:

Page 97:

Page 98:

Page 99:

Page 100:

Page 101:

Page 105:

Page 106:

Page 107:

Page 108:

Page 109:

Page 111:

Page 112:

Page 113:

Page 114:

Page 115:

Page 116:

Page 117:

Page 119:

Page 120:

Page 121:

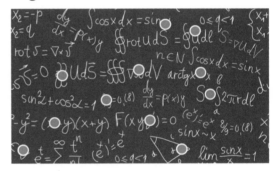

Page 122:

Page 123:

Page 124:

Page 125:

Page 126:

Page 127: